TO:

FROM:

DATE:

Christian art gifts®

Printed in Vietnam

DELIGHT YOURSELF IN THE LORD, AND HE WILL GIVE YOU THE DESIRES OF YOUR HEART. PS. 37:4

THE LORD IS MY LIGHT AND MY SALVATION–WHOM SHALL I FEAR? THE LORD IS THE STRONGHOLD OF MY LIFE–OF WHOM SHALL I BE AFRAID?

PS. 27:1

THE LORD HIMSELF GOES BEFORE YOU AND WILL BE WITH YOU;
HE WILL NEVER LEAVE YOU NOR FORSAKE YOU. DEUT. 31:8

GOD IS WORKING IN YOU, GIVING YOU THE DESIRE TO OBEY HIM AND THE POWER TO DO WHAT PLEASES HIM. PHIL. 2:13

I CAN DO EVERYTHING THROUGH CHRIST,
WHO GIVES ME STRENGTH. PHIL. 4:13

IF YOU WANT TO KNOW WHAT GOD WANTS YOU TO DO, ASK HIM, AND HE WILL GLADLY TELL YOU. JAMES 1:5

CREATE IN ME A PURE HEART, O GOD, AND RENEW A STEADFAST SPIRIT WITHIN ME. PS. 51:10

IF ANYONE IS IN CHRIST, HE IS A NEW CREATION;
THE OLD HAS GONE, THE NEW HAS COME! 2 COR. 5:17

CAST YOUR CARES ON THE LORD AND HE WILL SUSTAIN YOU.

PS. 55:22

THE LORD YOUR GOD IS WITH YOU, HE IS MIGHTY TO SAVE. HE WILL TAKE GREAT DELIGHT IN YOU, HE WILL QUIET YOU WITH HIS LOVE.

ZEPH. 3:17

THE LORD IS FAITHFUL TO ALL HIS PROMISES
AND LOVING TOWARD ALL HE HAS MADE. PS. 145:13

IN YOU, O LORD, DO I PUT MY TRUST. PS. 71:1

"BE STRONG AND COURAGEOUS . . . THE LORD YOUR GOD WILL BE WITH YOU WHEREVER YOU GO." JOSH. 1:9

DEPEND ON THE LORD IN WHATEVER YOU DO, AND YOUR PLANS WILL SUCCEED. PROV. 16:3

SINCE WE HAVE BEEN JUSTIFIED THROUGH FAITH, WE HAVE PEACE WITH GOD THROUGH OUR LORD JESUS CHRIST. ROM. 5:1

THE LORD IS MY ROCK, MY FORTRESS AND MY DELIVERER; MY GOD IS MY ROCK, IN WHOM I TAKE REFUGE. PS. 18:2

"IF ANYONE WOULD COME AFTER ME, HE MUST DENY HIMSELF AND TAKE UP HIS CROSS AND FOLLOW ME." MATT. 16:24

THE WORD OF THE LORD IS RIGHT AND TRUE;
HE IS FAITHFUL IN ALL HE DOES. PS. 33:4

THE LORD IS MY STRENGTH, MY SHIELD FROM EVERY DANGER. I TRUST IN HIM WITH ALL MY HEART. PS. 28:7

IN HIM WE HAVE REDEMPTION THROUGH HIS BLOOD, THE FORGIVENESS OF SINS, IN ACCORDANCE WITH THE RICHES OF GOD'S GRACE. EPH. 1:7

I TRUST IN YOUR UNFAILING LOVE. I WILL REJOICE
BECAUSE YOU HAVE RESCUED ME. PS. 13:5

LIVE A LIFE OF LOVE, JUST AS CHRIST LOVED US AND GAVE HIMSELF UP FOR US. EPH. 5:2

"YOU WILL SEEK ME AND FIND ME WHEN YOU SEEK ME WITH ALL YOUR HEART." JER. 29:13

MY SOUL FINDS REST IN GOD ALONE;
MY SALVATION COMES FROM HIM. PS. 62:1

DELIGHT YOURSELF IN THE LORD, AND HE WILL GIVE YOU THE DESIRES OF YOUR HEART. PS. 37:4

THE LORD IS MY LIGHT AND MY SALVATION–WHOM SHALL I FEAR? THE LORD IS THE STRONGHOLD OF MY LIFE–OF WHOM SHALL I BE AFRAID?

PS. 27:1

THE LORD HIMSELF GOES BEFORE YOU AND WILL BE WITH YOU;
HE WILL NEVER LEAVE YOU NOR FORSAKE YOU. DEUT. 31:8

GOD IS WORKING IN YOU, GIVING YOU THE DESIRE TO OBEY HIM AND THE POWER TO DO WHAT PLEASES HIM. PHIL. 2:13

I CAN DO EVERYTHING THROUGH CHRIST,
WHO GIVES ME STRENGTH. PHIL. 4:13

**IF YOU WANT TO KNOW WHAT GOD WANTS YOU TO DO,
ASK HIM, AND HE WILL GLADLY TELL YOU.** JAMES 1:5

CREATE IN ME A PURE HEART, O GOD, AND RENEW
A STEADFAST SPIRIT WITHIN ME. PS. 51:10

**IF ANYONE IS IN CHRIST, HE IS A NEW CREATION;
THE OLD HAS GONE, THE NEW HAS COME!** 2 COR. 5:17

CAST YOUR CARES ON THE LORD AND HE WILL SUSTAIN YOU.

PS. 55:22

THE LORD YOUR GOD IS WITH YOU, HE IS MIGHTY TO SAVE. HE WILL TAKE GREAT DELIGHT IN YOU, HE WILL QUIET YOU WITH HIS LOVE.

ZEPH. 3:17

THE LORD IS FAITHFUL TO ALL HIS PROMISES AND LOVING TOWARD ALL HE HAS MADE. PS. 145:13

IN YOU, O LORD, DO I PUT MY TRUST. PS. 71:1

"BE STRONG AND COURAGEOUS . . . THE LORD YOUR GOD WILL BE WITH YOU WHEREVER YOU GO." JOSH. 1:9

**DEPEND ON THE LORD IN WHATEVER YOU DO,
AND YOUR PLANS WILL SUCCEED.** PROV. 16:3

SINCE WE HAVE BEEN JUSTIFIED THROUGH FAITH, WE HAVE PEACE WITH GOD THROUGH OUR LORD JESUS CHRIST. ROM. 5:1

THE LORD IS MY ROCK, MY FORTRESS AND MY DELIVERER; MY GOD IS MY ROCK, IN WHOM I TAKE REFUGE. PS. 18:2

"IF ANYONE WOULD COME AFTER ME, HE MUST DENY HIMSELF AND TAKE UP HIS CROSS AND FOLLOW ME." MATT. 16:24

THE WORD OF THE LORD IS RIGHT AND TRUE;
HE IS FAITHFUL IN ALL HE DOES. PS. 33:4

THE LORD IS MY STRENGTH, MY SHIELD FROM EVERY DANGER. I TRUST IN HIM WITH ALL MY HEART. PS. 28:7

IN HIM WE HAVE REDEMPTION THROUGH HIS BLOOD, THE FORGIVENESS OF SINS, IN ACCORDANCE WITH THE RICHES OF GOD'S GRACE. EPH. 1:7

I TRUST IN YOUR UNFAILING LOVE. I WILL REJOICE BECAUSE YOU HAVE RESCUED ME. PS. 13:5

LIVE A LIFE OF LOVE, JUST AS CHRIST LOVED US AND GAVE HIMSELF UP FOR US. EPH. 5:2

"YOU WILL SEEK ME AND FIND ME WHEN YOU SEEK ME WITH ALL YOUR HEART." **JER. 29:13**

MY SOUL FINDS REST IN GOD ALONE;
MY SALVATION COMES FROM HIM. PS. 62:1

DELIGHT YOURSELF IN THE LORD, AND HE WILL GIVE YOU THE DESIRES OF YOUR HEART. PS. 37:4

THE LORD IS MY LIGHT AND MY SALVATION–WHOM SHALL I FEAR? THE LORD IS THE STRONGHOLD OF MY LIFE–OF WHOM SHALL I BE AFRAID?

PS. 27:1

THE LORD HIMSELF GOES BEFORE YOU AND WILL BE WITH YOU; HE WILL NEVER LEAVE YOU NOR FORSAKE YOU. DEUT. 31:8

GOD IS WORKING IN YOU, GIVING YOU THE DESIRE TO OBEY HIM AND THE POWER TO DO WHAT PLEASES HIM. PHIL. 2:13

I CAN DO EVERYTHING THROUGH CHRIST,
WHO GIVES ME STRENGTH. PHIL. 4:13

IF YOU WANT TO KNOW WHAT GOD WANTS YOU TO DO, ASK HIM, AND HE WILL GLADLY TELL YOU. JAMES 1:5

CREATE IN ME A PURE HEART, O GOD, AND RENEW A STEADFAST SPIRIT WITHIN ME. PS. 51:10

IF ANYONE IS IN CHRIST, HE IS A NEW CREATION; THE OLD HAS GONE, THE NEW HAS COME! 2 COR. 5:17

CAST YOUR CARES ON THE LORD AND HE WILL SUSTAIN YOU.

PS. 55:22

THE LORD YOUR GOD IS WITH YOU, HE IS MIGHTY TO SAVE. HE WILL TAKE GREAT DELIGHT IN YOU, HE WILL QUIET YOU WITH HIS LOVE.

ZEPH. 3:17

THE LORD IS FAITHFUL TO ALL HIS PROMISES
AND LOVING TOWARD ALL HE HAS MADE. PS. 145:13

IN YOU, O LORD, DO I PUT MY TRUST. PS. 71:1

"BE STRONG AND COURAGEOUS . . . THE LORD YOUR GOD WILL BE WITH YOU WHEREVER YOU GO." JOSH. 1:9

DEPEND ON THE LORD IN WHATEVER YOU DO,
AND YOUR PLANS WILL SUCCEED. PROV. 16:3

SINCE WE HAVE BEEN JUSTIFIED THROUGH FAITH, WE HAVE PEACE WITH GOD THROUGH OUR LORD JESUS CHRIST. ROM. 5:1

THE LORD IS MY ROCK, MY FORTRESS AND MY DELIVERER;
MY GOD IS MY ROCK, IN WHOM I TAKE REFUGE. PS. 18:2

“IF ANYONE WOULD COME AFTER ME, HE MUST DENY HIMSELF AND TAKE UP HIS CROSS AND FOLLOW ME.” MATT. 16:24

THE WORD OF THE LORD IS RIGHT AND TRUE;
HE IS FAITHFUL IN ALL HE DOES. PS. 33:4

THE LORD IS MY STRENGTH, MY SHIELD FROM EVERY DANGER. I TRUST IN HIM WITH ALL MY HEART. PS. 28:7

IN HIM WE HAVE REDEMPTION THROUGH HIS BLOOD, THE FORGIVENESS OF SINS, IN ACCORDANCE WITH THE RICHES OF GOD'S GRACE. EPH. 1:7

I TRUST IN YOUR UNFAILING LOVE. I WILL REJOICE BECAUSE YOU HAVE RESCUED ME. PS. 13:5

LIVE A LIFE OF LOVE, JUST AS CHRIST LOVED US AND GAVE HIMSELF UP FOR US. EPH. 5:2

"YOU WILL SEEK ME AND FIND ME WHEN YOU SEEK ME WITH ALL YOUR HEART." JER. 29:13

MY SOUL FINDS REST IN GOD ALONE;
MY SALVATION COMES FROM HIM. PS. 62:1

DELIGHT YOURSELF IN THE LORD, AND HE WILL GIVE YOU THE DESIRES OF YOUR HEART. PS. 37:4

THE LORD IS MY LIGHT AND MY SALVATION–WHOM SHALL I FEAR? THE LORD IS THE STRONGHOLD OF MY LIFE–OF WHOM SHALL I BE AFRAID?

PS. 27:1

**THE LORD HIMSELF GOES BEFORE YOU AND WILL BE WITH YOU;
HE WILL NEVER LEAVE YOU NOR FORSAKE YOU.** DEUT. 31:8

GOD IS WORKING IN YOU, GIVING YOU THE DESIRE TO OBEY HIM AND THE POWER TO DO WHAT PLEASES HIM. PHIL. 2:13

I CAN DO EVERYTHING THROUGH CHRIST, WHO GIVES ME STRENGTH. PHIL. 4:13

IF YOU WANT TO KNOW WHAT GOD WANTS YOU TO DO, ASK HIM, AND HE WILL GLADLY TELL YOU. JAMES 1:5

CREATE IN ME A PURE HEART, O GOD, AND RENEW A STEADFAST SPIRIT WITHIN ME. PS. 51:10

IF ANYONE IS IN CHRIST, HE IS A NEW CREATION;
THE OLD HAS GONE, THE NEW HAS COME! 2 COR. 5:17

CAST YOUR CARES ON THE LORD AND HE WILL SUSTAIN YOU.

PS. 55:22

THE LORD YOUR GOD IS WITH YOU, HE IS MIGHTY TO SAVE. HE WILL TAKE GREAT DELIGHT IN YOU, HE WILL QUIET YOU WITH HIS LOVE.

ZEPH. 3:17

THE LORD IS FAITHFUL TO ALL HIS PROMISES
AND LOVING TOWARD ALL HE HAS MADE. PS. 145:13

IN YOU, O LORD, DO I PUT MY TRUST. PS. 71:1

"BE STRONG AND COURAGEOUS . . . THE LORD YOUR GOD WILL BE WITH YOU WHEREVER YOU GO." JOSH. 1:9

DEPEND ON THE LORD IN WHATEVER YOU DO,
AND YOUR PLANS WILL SUCCEED. PROV. 16:3

SINCE WE HAVE BEEN JUSTIFIED THROUGH FAITH, WE HAVE PEACE WITH GOD THROUGH OUR LORD JESUS CHRIST. ROM. 5:1

**THE LORD IS MY ROCK, MY FORTRESS AND MY DELIVERER;
MY GOD IS MY ROCK, IN WHOM I TAKE REFUGE.** PS. 18:2

"IF ANYONE WOULD COME AFTER ME, HE MUST DENY HIMSELF AND TAKE UP HIS CROSS AND FOLLOW ME." MATT. 16:24

THE WORD OF THE LORD IS RIGHT AND TRUE;
HE IS FAITHFUL IN ALL HE DOES. PS. 33:4

THE LORD IS MY STRENGTH, MY SHIELD FROM EVERY DANGER.
I TRUST IN HIM WITH ALL MY HEART. PS. 28:7

IN HIM WE HAVE REDEMPTION THROUGH HIS BLOOD, THE FORGIVENESS OF SINS, IN ACCORDANCE WITH THE RICHES OF GOD'S GRACE. EPH. 1:7

I TRUST IN YOUR UNFAILING LOVE. I WILL REJOICE BECAUSE YOU HAVE RESCUED ME. PS. 13:5

LIVE A LIFE OF LOVE, JUST AS CHRIST LOVED US
AND GAVE HIMSELF UP FOR US. EPH. 5:2

"YOU WILL SEEK ME AND FIND ME WHEN YOU SEEK ME WITH ALL YOUR HEART." JER. 29:13

MY SOUL FINDS REST IN GOD ALONE;
MY SALVATION COMES FROM HIM. PS. 62:1

DELIGHT YOURSELF IN THE LORD, AND HE WILL GIVE YOU THE DESIRES OF YOUR HEART. PS. 37:4

THE LORD IS MY LIGHT AND MY SALVATION–WHOM SHALL I FEAR? THE LORD IS THE STRONGHOLD OF MY LIFE–OF WHOM SHALL I BE AFRAID?

PS. 27:1

THE LORD HIMSELF GOES BEFORE YOU AND WILL BE WITH YOU;
HE WILL NEVER LEAVE YOU NOR FORSAKE YOU. DEUT. 31:8

GOD IS WORKING IN YOU, GIVING YOU THE DESIRE TO OBEY HIM AND THE POWER TO DO WHAT PLEASES HIM. PHIL. 2:13

I CAN DO EVERYTHING THROUGH CHRIST,
WHO GIVES ME STRENGTH. PHIL. 4:13

IF YOU WANT TO KNOW WHAT GOD WANTS YOU TO DO, ASK HIM, AND HE WILL GLADLY TELL YOU. JAMES 1:5

CREATE IN ME A PURE HEART, O GOD, AND RENEW
A STEADFAST SPIRIT WITHIN ME. PS. 51:10

IF ANYONE IS IN CHRIST, HE IS A NEW CREATION;
THE OLD HAS GONE, THE NEW HAS COME! 2 COR. 5:17

CAST YOUR CARES ON THE LORD AND HE WILL SUSTAIN YOU.

PS. 55:22

THE LORD YOUR GOD IS WITH YOU, HE IS MIGHTY TO SAVE. HE WILL TAKE GREAT DELIGHT IN YOU, HE WILL QUIET YOU WITH HIS LOVE.

ZEPH. 3:17

THE LORD IS FAITHFUL TO ALL HIS PROMISES AND LOVING TOWARD ALL HE HAS MADE. PS. 145:13

IN YOU, O LORD, DO I PUT MY TRUST. PS. 71:1

"BE STRONG AND COURAGEOUS . . . THE LORD YOUR GOD WILL BE WITH YOU WHEREVER YOU GO." JOSH. 1:9

DEPEND ON THE LORD IN WHATEVER YOU DO, AND YOUR PLANS WILL SUCCEED. PROV. 16:3

SINCE WE HAVE BEEN JUSTIFIED THROUGH FAITH, WE HAVE PEACE WITH GOD THROUGH OUR LORD JESUS CHRIST. ROM. 5:1

THE LORD IS MY ROCK, MY FORTRESS AND MY DELIVERER;
MY GOD IS MY ROCK, IN WHOM I TAKE REFUGE. PS. 18:2

"IF ANYONE WOULD COME AFTER ME, HE MUST DENY HIMSELF AND TAKE UP HIS CROSS AND FOLLOW ME." MATT. 16:24

THE WORD OF THE LORD IS RIGHT AND TRUE;
HE IS FAITHFUL IN ALL HE DOES. PS. 33:4

THE LORD IS MY STRENGTH, MY SHIELD FROM EVERY DANGER.
I TRUST IN HIM WITH ALL MY HEART. PS. 28:7

IN HIM WE HAVE REDEMPTION THROUGH HIS BLOOD, THE FORGIVENESS OF SINS, IN ACCORDANCE WITH THE RICHES OF GOD'S GRACE. EPH. 1:7

I TRUST IN YOUR UNFAILING LOVE. I WILL REJOICE
BECAUSE YOU HAVE RESCUED ME. PS. 13:5

LIVE A LIFE OF LOVE, JUST AS CHRIST LOVED US
AND GAVE HIMSELF UP FOR US. EPH. 5:2

"YOU WILL SEEK ME AND FIND ME WHEN YOU SEEK ME WITH ALL YOUR HEART." JER. 29:13

MY SOUL FINDS REST IN GOD ALONE;
MY SALVATION COMES FROM HIM. PS. 62:1

DELIGHT YOURSELF IN THE LORD, AND HE WILL GIVE YOU THE DESIRES OF YOUR HEART. PS. 37:4

THE LORD IS MY LIGHT AND MY SALVATION–WHOM SHALL I FEAR? THE LORD IS THE STRONGHOLD OF MY LIFE–OF WHOM SHALL I BE AFRAID?

PS. 27:1

THE LORD HIMSELF GOES BEFORE YOU AND WILL BE WITH YOU; HE WILL NEVER LEAVE YOU NOR FORSAKE YOU. DEUT. 31:8

GOD IS WORKING IN YOU, GIVING YOU THE DESIRE TO OBEY HIM AND THE POWER TO DO WHAT PLEASES HIM. PHIL. 2:13

I CAN DO EVERYTHING THROUGH CHRIST,

WHO GIVES ME STRENGTH. PHIL. 4:13

IF YOU WANT TO KNOW WHAT GOD WANTS YOU TO DO, ASK HIM, AND HE WILL GLADLY TELL YOU. JAMES 1:5

CREATE IN ME A PURE HEART, O GOD, AND RENEW A STEADFAST SPIRIT WITHIN ME. PS. 51:10

IF ANYONE IS IN CHRIST, HE IS A NEW CREATION;
THE OLD HAS GONE, THE NEW HAS COME! 2 COR. 5:17

CAST YOUR CARES ON THE LORD AND HE WILL SUSTAIN YOU.

PS. 55:22

THE LORD YOUR GOD IS WITH YOU, HE IS MIGHTY TO SAVE. HE WILL TAKE GREAT DELIGHT IN YOU, HE WILL QUIET YOU WITH HIS LOVE.

ZEPH. 3:17

THE LORD IS FAITHFUL TO ALL HIS PROMISES
AND LOVING TOWARD ALL HE HAS MADE. PS. 145:13

IN YOU, O LORD, DO I PUT MY TRUST. PS. 71:1

"BE STRONG AND COURAGEOUS . . . THE LORD YOUR GOD WILL BE WITH YOU WHEREVER YOU GO." JOSH. 1:9

**DEPEND ON THE LORD IN WHATEVER YOU DO,
AND YOUR PLANS WILL SUCCEED.** PROV. 16:3

SINCE WE HAVE BEEN JUSTIFIED THROUGH FAITH, WE HAVE PEACE WITH GOD THROUGH OUR LORD JESUS CHRIST. ROM. 5:1

THE LORD IS MY ROCK, MY FORTRESS AND MY DELIVERER; MY GOD IS MY ROCK, IN WHOM I TAKE REFUGE. PS. 18:2

"IF ANYONE WOULD COME AFTER ME, HE MUST DENY HIMSELF AND TAKE UP HIS CROSS AND FOLLOW ME." MATT. 16:24

THE WORD OF THE LORD IS RIGHT AND TRUE;
HE IS FAITHFUL IN ALL HE DOES. PS. 33:4

THE LORD IS MY STRENGTH, MY SHIELD FROM EVERY DANGER.
I TRUST IN HIM WITH ALL MY HEART. PS. 28:7

IN HIM WE HAVE REDEMPTION THROUGH HIS BLOOD, THE FORGIVENESS OF SINS, IN ACCORDANCE WITH THE RICHES OF GOD'S GRACE. EPH. 1:7

I TRUST IN YOUR UNFAILING LOVE. I WILL REJOICE BECAUSE YOU HAVE RESCUED ME. PS. 13:5

LIVE A LIFE OF LOVE, JUST AS CHRIST LOVED US AND GAVE HIMSELF UP FOR US. EPH. 5:2

"YOU WILL SEEK ME AND FIND ME WHEN YOU SEEK ME WITH ALL YOUR HEART." JER. 29:13

MY SOUL FINDS REST IN GOD ALONE;
MY SALVATION COMES FROM HIM. PS. 62:1

DELIGHT YOURSELF IN THE LORD, AND HE WILL
GIVE YOU THE DESIRES OF YOUR HEART. PS. 37:4

THE LORD IS MY LIGHT AND MY SALVATION–WHOM SHALL I FEAR? THE LORD IS THE STRONGHOLD OF MY LIFE–OF WHOM SHALL I BE AFRAID?

PS. 27:1

THE LORD HIMSELF GOES BEFORE YOU AND WILL BE WITH YOU;
HE WILL NEVER LEAVE YOU NOR FORSAKE YOU. DEUT. 31:8

GOD IS WORKING IN YOU, GIVING YOU THE DESIRE TO OBEY HIM AND THE POWER TO DO WHAT PLEASES HIM. PHIL. 2:13

I CAN DO EVERYTHING THROUGH CHRIST,
WHO GIVES ME STRENGTH. PHIL. 4:13

IF YOU WANT TO KNOW WHAT GOD WANTS YOU TO DO, ASK HIM, AND HE WILL GLADLY TELL YOU. JAMES 1:5

CREATE IN ME A PURE HEART, O GOD, AND RENEW A STEADFAST SPIRIT WITHIN ME. PS. 51:10

IF ANYONE IS IN CHRIST, HE IS A NEW CREATION; THE OLD HAS GONE, THE NEW HAS COME! 2 COR. 5:17

CAST YOUR CARES ON THE LORD AND HE WILL SUSTAIN YOU.

PS. 55:22

THE LORD YOUR GOD IS WITH YOU, HE IS MIGHTY TO SAVE. HE WILL TAKE GREAT DELIGHT IN YOU, HE WILL QUIET YOU WITH HIS LOVE.

ZEPH. 3:17

THE LORD IS FAITHFUL TO ALL HIS PROMISES
AND LOVING TOWARD ALL HE HAS MADE. PS. 145:13

IN YOU, O LORD, DO I PUT MY TRUST. PS. 71:1

"BE STRONG AND COURAGEOUS . . . THE LORD YOUR GOD WILL BE WITH YOU WHEREVER YOU GO." JOSH. 1:9

DEPEND ON THE LORD IN WHATEVER YOU DO,
AND YOUR PLANS WILL SUCCEED. PROV. 16:3

SINCE WE HAVE BEEN JUSTIFIED THROUGH FAITH, WE HAVE PEACE WITH GOD THROUGH OUR LORD JESUS CHRIST. ROM. 5:1

THE LORD IS MY ROCK, MY FORTRESS AND MY DELIVERER; MY GOD IS MY ROCK, IN WHOM I TAKE REFUGE. PS. 18:2

"IF ANYONE WOULD COME AFTER ME, HE MUST DENY HIMSELF AND TAKE UP HIS CROSS AND FOLLOW ME." MATT. 16:24

THE WORD OF THE LORD IS RIGHT AND TRUE;
HE IS FAITHFUL IN ALL HE DOES. PS. 33:4

THE LORD IS MY STRENGTH, MY SHIELD FROM EVERY DANGER.
I TRUST IN HIM WITH ALL MY HEART. PS. 28:7

IN HIM WE HAVE REDEMPTION THROUGH HIS BLOOD, THE FORGIVENESS OF SINS, IN ACCORDANCE WITH THE RICHES OF GOD'S GRACE. EPH. 1:7

I TRUST IN YOUR UNFAILING LOVE. I WILL REJOICE BECAUSE YOU HAVE RESCUED ME. PS. 13:5

LIVE A LIFE OF LOVE, JUST AS CHRIST LOVED US AND GAVE HIMSELF UP FOR US. EPH. 5:2

"YOU WILL SEEK ME AND FIND ME WHEN YOU SEEK ME WITH ALL YOUR HEART." JER. 29:13

MY SOUL FINDS REST IN GOD ALONE;
MY SALVATION COMES FROM HIM. PS. 62:1

DELIGHT YOURSELF IN THE LORD, AND HE WILL GIVE YOU THE DESIRES OF YOUR HEART. PS. 37:4

THE LORD IS MY LIGHT AND MY SALVATION–WHOM SHALL I FEAR? THE LORD IS THE STRONGHOLD OF MY LIFE–OF WHOM SHALL I BE AFRAID?

PS. 27:1

THE LORD HIMSELF GOES BEFORE YOU AND WILL BE WITH YOU;
HE WILL NEVER LEAVE YOU NOR FORSAKE YOU. DEUT. 31:8

GOD IS WORKING IN YOU, GIVING YOU THE DESIRE TO OBEY HIM AND THE POWER TO DO WHAT PLEASES HIM. PHIL. 2:13

I CAN DO EVERYTHING THROUGH CHRIST,
WHO GIVES ME STRENGTH. PHIL. 4:13

IF YOU WANT TO KNOW WHAT GOD WANTS YOU TO DO, ASK HIM, AND HE WILL GLADLY TELL YOU. JAMES 1:5

CREATE IN ME A PURE HEART, O GOD, AND RENEW
A STEADFAST SPIRIT WITHIN ME. PS. 51:10

IF ANYONE IS IN CHRIST, HE IS A NEW CREATION;
THE OLD HAS GONE, THE NEW HAS COME! 2 COR. 5:17

CAST YOUR CARES ON THE LORD AND HE WILL SUSTAIN YOU.

PS. 55:22

THE LORD YOUR GOD IS WITH YOU, HE IS MIGHTY TO SAVE. HE WILL TAKE GREAT DELIGHT IN YOU, HE WILL QUIET YOU WITH HIS LOVE.

ZEPH. 3:17

THE LORD IS FAITHFUL TO ALL HIS PROMISES
AND LOVING TOWARD ALL HE HAS MADE. PS. 145:13

IN YOU, O LORD, DO I PUT MY TRUST. PS. 71:1

"BE STRONG AND COURAGEOUS . . . THE LORD YOUR GOD WILL BE WITH YOU WHEREVER YOU GO." JOSH. 1:9

DEPEND ON THE LORD IN WHATEVER YOU DO,
AND YOUR PLANS WILL SUCCEED. PROV. 16:3

SINCE WE HAVE BEEN JUSTIFIED THROUGH FAITH, WE HAVE PEACE WITH GOD THROUGH OUR LORD JESUS CHRIST. **ROM. 5:1**

THE LORD IS MY ROCK, MY FORTRESS AND MY DELIVERER; MY GOD IS MY ROCK, IN WHOM I TAKE REFUGE. PS. 18:2

"IF ANYONE WOULD COME AFTER ME, HE MUST DENY HIMSELF AND TAKE UP HIS CROSS AND FOLLOW ME." MATT. 16:24

THE WORD OF THE LORD IS RIGHT AND TRUE;
HE IS FAITHFUL IN ALL HE DOES. PS. 33:4

THE LORD IS MY STRENGTH, MY SHIELD FROM EVERY DANGER.
I TRUST IN HIM WITH ALL MY HEART. PS. 28:7

IN HIM WE HAVE REDEMPTION THROUGH HIS BLOOD, THE FORGIVENESS OF SINS, IN ACCORDANCE WITH THE RICHES OF GOD'S GRACE. EPH. 1:7

I TRUST IN YOUR UNFAILING LOVE. I WILL REJOICE
BECAUSE YOU HAVE RESCUED ME. PS. 13:5

LIVE A LIFE OF LOVE, JUST AS CHRIST LOVED US AND GAVE HIMSELF UP FOR US. EPH. 5:2

"YOU WILL SEEK ME AND FIND ME WHEN YOU SEEK ME WITH ALL YOUR HEART." JER. 29:13

MY SOUL FINDS REST IN GOD ALONE;
MY SALVATION COMES FROM HIM. PS. 62:1